Percussion
Exam Pieces & Studies
ABRSM Grade 3
Selected from the syllabus from 2020

Name

Date of exa

CW00386169

Contents
page

Pieces

SNARE DRUM

1	**William Edwards** Out of Line SOLO	2
2	**Rachel Gledhill** Jazz Waltz for Two SOLO	3
3	**Kevin Hathway** Stick Insect	4
4	**David Hext** Tango Twister	6
5	**Zara Nunn** Clock-watching	7

TIMPANI

1	**Jan Bradley** Arriving in Style	8
2	**Lizzie Davis** Waltz of the Warlocks	10
3	**Damien Harron** Tresillo SOLO	11
4	**Ian Wright** Bouncing Beethoven SOLO	12
5	**Andrew J. Smith** Celebration	14

TUNED PERCUSSION

1	**Alan Bullard** Spring Awakening SOLO	15
2	**David Hext** Spicy Sauce	16
3	**William Edwards** After Dark SOLO	18
4	**Arthur C. Lipner** Swing Steps	19
5	**Cameron Sinclair** Spiral	20

Studies

Study A for snare drum	22
Study B for snare drum	23
Study A for timpani	24
Study B for timpani	24

These are a selection of pieces set for Grade 3. The full list is provided in the Percussion Syllabus, which can be found online at www.abrsm.org/percussion.

Editorial guidance
Where appropriate, we have edited the pieces and studies to help you prepare for your performance. Printed editorial suggestions such as sticking, metronome marks, etc. are for guidance only and do not need to be strictly observed.

First published in 2019 by ABRSM (Publishing) Ltd,
a wholly owned subsidiary of ABRSM, 4 London Wall Place,
London EC2Y 5AU, United Kingdom
© 2019 by The Associated Board of the Royal Schools of Music
Distributed worldwide by Oxford University Press

Music origination by Moira Roach
Cover by Kate Benjamin & Andy Potts, with thanks to Brighton College
Printed in England by Caligraving Ltd, Thetford, Norfolk, on materials from sustainable sources.
P14588

SNARE DRUM

Out of Line

For solo snare drum

William Edwards
(born 1991)

With flair ♩ = 100

AB 3958

Jazz Waltz for Two

Solo for snare drum and low tom

Rachel Gledhill
(born 1966)

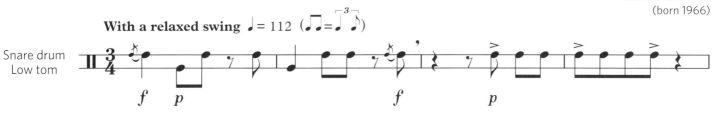

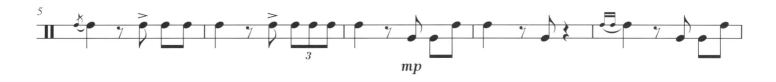

Stick Insect

Duet for snare drum and low tom

Kevin Hathway
(born 1953)

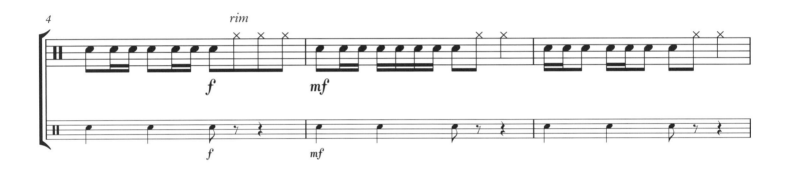

AB 3958

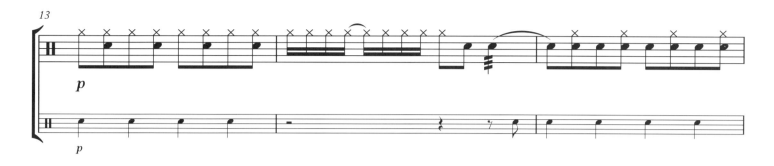

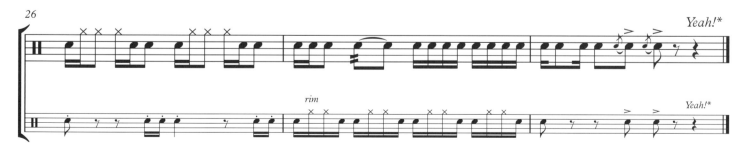

* Optional shout by both players.

Tango Twister

For snare drum and piano

David Hext
(born 1963)

Clock-watching

For snare drum and piano

Zara Nunn
(born 1973)

With a continuing sense of urgency ♩. = 60

p *poco a poco cresc.*

mf

f *sfz*

f

sfz

Arriving in Style

Duet for timpani and snare drum or low tom

Jan Bradley
(born 1974)

AB 3958

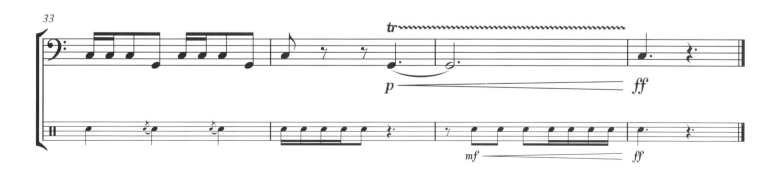

TIMPANI

Waltz of the Warlocks

For timpani and piano

Lizzie Davis
(born 1947)

accel. al fine

AB 3958

Tresillo

For solo timpani

Damien Harron
(born 1971)

Bouncing Beethoven

For solo timpani

Ian Wright
(born 1944)

AB 3958

Celebration

For timpani and piano

Andrew J. Smith
(born 1985)

AB 3958

Spring Awakening

For solo tuned percussion

Alan Bullard
(born 1947)

Spicy Sauce

Duet for xylophone and untuned percussion

David Hext
(born 1963)

The timbale part may alternatively be played on two snare drums (with snares off) at different pitches.

AB 3958

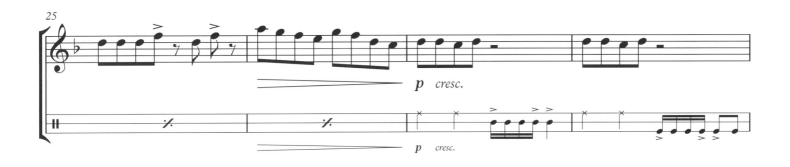

After Dark

For solo tuned percussion

William Edwards
(born 1991)

AB 3958

Swing Steps

For tuned percussion and piano

Arthur C. Lipner
(born 1958)

Spiral

For xylophone or marimba and piano

Cameron Sinclair
(born 1964)

AB 3958

Study A

For snare drum

Rudiments   multiple bounce roll, single-stroke four, single-stroke seven, flam, ruff

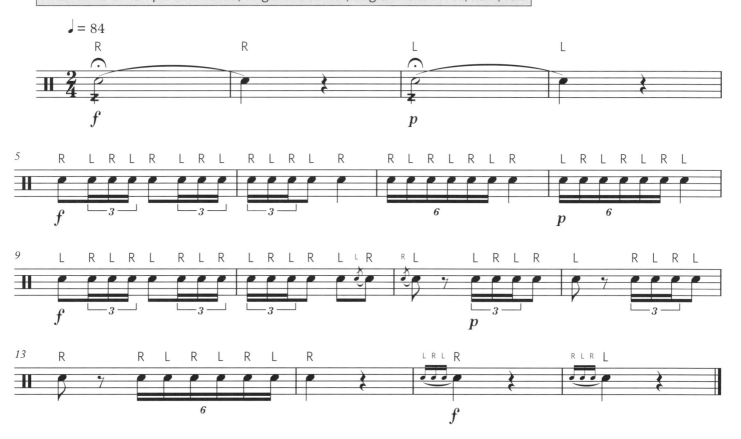

AB 3958

Study B

For snare drum

Rudiments seven-stroke roll, thirteen-stroke roll, ruff, fifteen-stroke roll

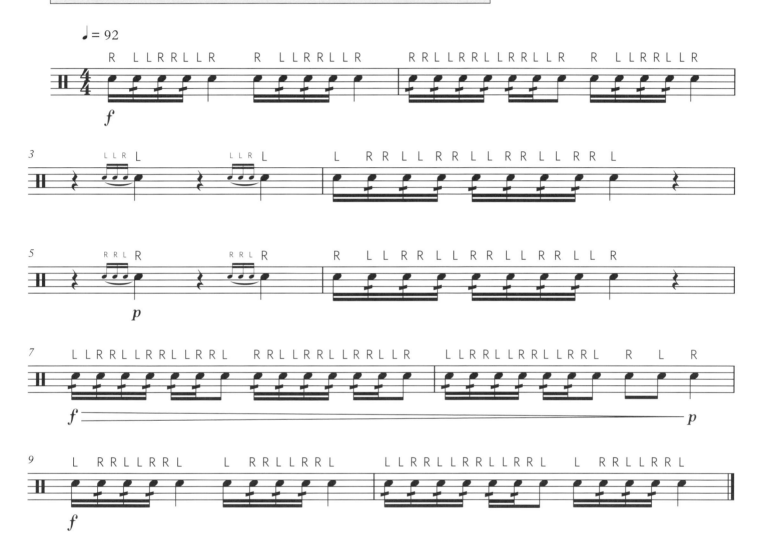

Study A

For timpani

Study B

For timpani

AB 3958